A COLLECTORS BOOK ON

TOOTHPICK HOLDERS

by
Florence Mighell

I buy books and more books, but all I do is look at the pictures. I am sure there are many others like myself. So this is a book composed mainly of pictures, but I have tried to incorporate some pertinent information.

I do not profess to be an authority on anything in the collecting field, including toothpick holders. I am just a spokesman for the many who have chosen to collect and cherish toothpick holders. It was my good fortune to have a collection at my disposal to photograph and research.

The purpose of this book is to enable collectors to identify more readily their holders. I have tried my utmost to title correctly each piece with the resources available, but I am not infallible. If in error, I apologize. I christened those items for which I could not find data. Thus they will remain so identified until I am corrected. I would appreciate any information or correspondence.

Happy Hunting,

Florence Mighell

KEY TO REFERENCE ABBREVIATIONS

Boultinghouse	Art and Colored Glass Toothpick Holders	Boul.
Kamm	Pitcher Book I through VIII	Kamm
Metz	Early American Pattern Glass I and II	Metz
Lee	Victorian Glass	Lee V
Lee	Early American Pattern Glass	Lee P
Herreck	Greentown Glass Book	Herr.
Peterson	Salt and Salt Shakers I and II	Pet.
Millard	Opaque Glass	Mill. O
Millard	Goblets I and II	Mill. G
Warman	Milk Glass Addenda	War. M
Warman	Price Guide	War. P
Brahmer	Custard Book	Bra.
Page		p.
Plate		pl.
Named by author		*

PLATE I

FIRST ROW

Amberina, Inverted Thumbprint ----------------------------Boul., pl. 3
Amberina, Daisy/Button ------------------------------------Boul., pl. 2
Baccarat Swirl
Amberina, Enamel Flower
Baccarat

SECOND ROW

Cranberry, Ribbed, Bulbous, Flange Top
Findlay, Onyx ---Boul., pl. 101
Ribbed Swirl, Frosted Base, Blue Top
Millefiori
Cranberry, Mary Gregory

THIRD ROW

Burmese, Enamel Daisy
Satin, Embossed Scroll, H. P. Violets
Mother of Pearl, Diamond Quilt -------------------------Boul., pl. 156
Satin, Beaded Top --Boul., pl. 220
Agata

FOURTH ROW

Opalesent Diamond Point, Signed Baccarat ---------------Boul., pl. 85
Satin, Embossed Scroll, Beaded Top, H. P. Flower
Clear Coin Spot
Satin Swirl, Beaded Top, Enamel Flowers
Cranberry

FIFTH ROW

Satin, Signed Libby --Boul., pl. 220
Bulbous, Enamel, Signed Baden Wieler -------------------Boul., pl. 32
Pomona, Tricorner ---Boul., pl. 180
Bulbous, Enamel ---Boul., pl. 32
Satin, Garlic Clove

SIXTH ROW

Windows, Clear and Opalescent ---------------------------Boul., pl. 277
Tiffany, Signed --Boul., pl. 7
End of Day
Aventurine
Enamelled Flower, Signed Galle

PLATE II

PLATE III

Between 1890 and 1900, the U.S. Glass Co. created a number of pressed glass patterns and named them after the states. There were also patterns called "The States," "United States," and "America."

I do not know if a pattern was made for each state or if toothpick holders were made in all the state patterns they did produce. These are my findings thus far.

FIRST ROW

Alabama --Kamm I, p. 81
Kansas, Jewel With Dewdrops -----------------------Kamm I, p. 78
The States --Kamm V, p. 142
Kentucky --Kamm IV, p. 68
Pennsylvania, Hand ---------------------------------Kamm III, p. 9

SECOND ROW

Virginia, Banded Portland ----------------------------Kamm II, p. 89
Virginia, Banded Portland
Virginia --Kamm III, p. 89
Michigan, Inverted --------------------------------Kamm I, p. 106
Michigan, Panelled Jewel
Michigan

THIRD ROW

Florida, Sunken Primrose -----------------------------Kamm IV, p. 73
Illinois --War. P
Minnesota --Kamm VIII, p. 51
California, Beaded Grape ---------------------------Kamm IV, p. 94
Carolina ---Kamm II, p. 28

FOURTH ROW

New Hampshire, Bent Buckle, Maiden's Blush --------Kamm III, p. 97
New Hampshire, Bent Buckle -----------------------Kamm III, p. 97
+ Texas --Kamm II, p. 58
Washington --War. P
Vermont ---Kamm VI, p. 56

FIFTH ROW

Colorado --Kamm II, p. 115
Wisconsin, Beaded Dewdrop --------------------------Kamm VII, p. 46
Colorado --Kamm II, p. 115

SIXTH ROW

Tennessee, Jewel and Crescent -----------------------Kamm III, p. 62
Delaware, Cranberry ---------------------------------Kamm I, p. 103
Delaware, Clear/Gold
Delaware, Green

PLATE IV

FIRST ROW

Klondike, Frosted Amberette, Dalzell, Gilmore and
    Leighton Co., Findlay, Ohio, Circa 1897 _____Kamm VI, pl. 15
Columbian Coin _____Boul., pl. 234
Coin Frosted, Central Glass Co., Wheeling, W. Va.,
    Circa 1892 _____Kamm III, p. 80
Coin Clear, Central Glass Co.
Klondike Clear _____Kamm VI, pl. 15

SECOND ROW

*Star in Square with Fans
Orinda, National Glass Co., 1901 _____Kamm V, p. 111
Pickett Fence, Maker Unknown, Circa 1880 _____Kamm I, p. 88
Rib and Bead, Maker and Date Unknown _____Kamm VIII, p. 60
*Star in Diamond with Fan

THIRD ROW

Beaded Swirl and Disc, Maker and Date Unknown ____Kamm VIII, p. 36
Star in Square, Maker and Date Unknown _____Kamm VIII, p. 48
Jewel with Moon and Star (Shrine), Maker and
    Date Unknown _____Kamm I, p. 101
*Waldo
Heisey's No. 343½, Signed, A. H. Heisey,
    Newark, Ohio, 1905 _____Kamm VII, pl. 41

FOURTH ROW

Riverside, Riverside Glass Co.,
    Wellsburg, W. Va., 1890 _____Kamm VIII, p. 35
Tacoma, Greensburg Glass Co., 1894 _____Kamm VI, p. 39
Priscilla Dalzell, Gilmore and Leighton Co., 1896 _____Kamm IV, p. 92
Eight-o-Eight, Maker and Date Unknown _____Kamm IV, p. 78
*Banded Double Thumbprint

FIFTH ROW

Atlanta (Square Lion), Fostoria Glass Co.,
    Fostoria, Ohio, 1890 _____Kamm V, p. 83
Block and Star, Maker Unknown, 1885 _____Kamm I, p. 43
*Intaglio Flower
*Jack
**Rosemary

SIXTH ROW

*Pretty Prairie
Imperials No. 77, Imperial Glass Co., 1894 _____Kamm VII, p. 66
Duncan and Miller No. 42, Duncan and Miller Glass Co.,
    Washington, Pa. _____Kamm VII, p. 33
Stars and Stripes, Advertised Montgomery Ward, 1899 ___Kamm II, p. 70
Fancy Cut, Maker and Date Unknown _____Kamm II, p. 103

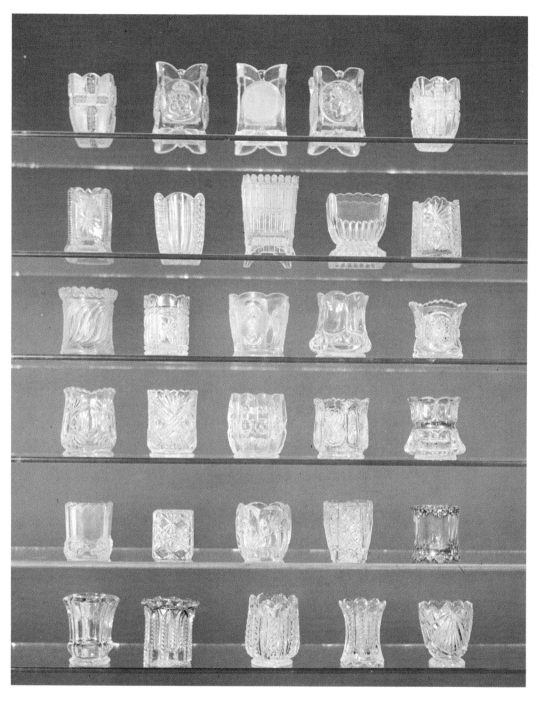

PLATE V

FIRST ROW
Fish _____Kamm VIII, pl. 31
Trench Mortar _____Boul., pl. 264; Kamm VIII, pl. 30
Chair, Daisy/Button
Bird in Tree Stump _____Boul., pl. 20
Monkey and Hat

SECOND ROW
Gypsy Kettle, Cane
Rabbit with Basket
Rabbit in Tree
Baby Buggy
Bird in Cup _____Boul., pl. 20

THIRD ROW
Anvil, Diamond Point
Handled Basket
Kettle _____Boul., pl. 140
Handled Barrel
Anvil, Daisy/Button

FOURTH ROW
Gypsy Kettle, Cane Flange
Anvil, Daisy/Button
Gypsy Kettle, Ruby Flash, Cane Flange

FIFTH ROW
Boot
Boot on Sandwich Star Base
Baby Shoe
Boot on Sandwich Star Base
Boot

SIXTH ROW
Bird in Egg Shell
Boot
Basket _____Lee V, pl. 104
Monkey on Tree Stump _____Lee V, pl. 104

PLATE VI

FIRST ROW

Panelled Agave, Cactus, Greentown _____Boul., pl. 51
Hand, Opaque, Greentown Glass Co. _____Boul., pl. 123
Boy with Pack, Opaque _____Boul., pl. 26
Rip Van Winkle, Opaque, Signed Portieux
Panelled Agave, Cactus, Greentown

SECOND ROW

Inverted Fan and Feather, Custard
Chrysanthemum Sprig, Custard, Signed Northwood
Little Gem, Opaque
Chrysanthemum Sprig, Signed Northwood
Geneva, Custard

THIRD ROW

*Margaret
Ivorina Verde
Wild Bouquet
*Plain Jane
Flower Flange

FOURTH ROW

Swirl Pot
Square Urn with Ring
Flying Fish
Square Urn with Ring
Gypsy Pot

FIFTH ROW

Footed Urn
Three Handled Urn
Oblong Container, English Register
Square Urn with Ring
Round Urn with Ring, Vogue Merc. Co., New York, N. Y.

SIXTH ROW

Signed Akro
Hand Urn
Leaf Urn
Wheelbarrow, Greentown
Round Urn with Ring, Vogue Merc. Co., New York, N. Y.
Octagon
Yellow Slag

PLATE VII

Many makers of fine porcelain are listed in reference books but not all were makers of the lowly toothpick holder. Some of the following were identified by their markings.

FIRST ROW

Jack and the Beanstock ------------------------------Royal Bayreuth
Corinthian Ware ----------------------------------Royal Bayreuth
Davenport
Corinthian Ware ----------------------------------Royal Bayreuth
Two Ladies with Sheep ----------------------------Royal Bayreuth

SECOND ROW

White and Red Rose --------------------------------Royal Bayreuth
Huntress with Dogs --------------------------------Royal Bayreuth
Sunbonnet Babies ----------------------------------Royal Bayreuth
Bouquet of Violets --------------------------------Royal Bayreuth
Rose Tapestry -------------------------------------Royal Bayreuth

THIRD ROW

Carnations, Three Handles, Satin Finish ----------------R. S. Prussia
Roses, Two Handles -------------------------------R. S. Prussia
Mill Wheel, Two Handles --------------------------------Unsigned
Water Lily, Two Handles --------------------------R. S. Prussia
Flowers, Three Handles ---------------------------------Unsigned

FOURTH ROW

White Rose, Three Handles ------------------------R. S. Germany
Red and Pink Roses, Two Handles --------------------R. S. Prussia
Three Handles ------------------------------------Royal Worcester
Red Flowers, Two Handles --------------------------R. S. Prussia
Flowers, Two Handles -----------------------------R. S. Germany

FIFTH ROW

Boat Shape, Apple Blossom ------------------------R. S. Germany
Blank, Three Handles -----------------------------R. S. Germany
Boat Shape, Carnations ---------------------------R. S. Germany

SIXTH ROW

Gainsborough ---Spode
Two Handles --------------------------------------Royal Worcester
Camilla ---Spode
Two Handles --------------------------------------Royal Worcester
Urn ---Unsigned

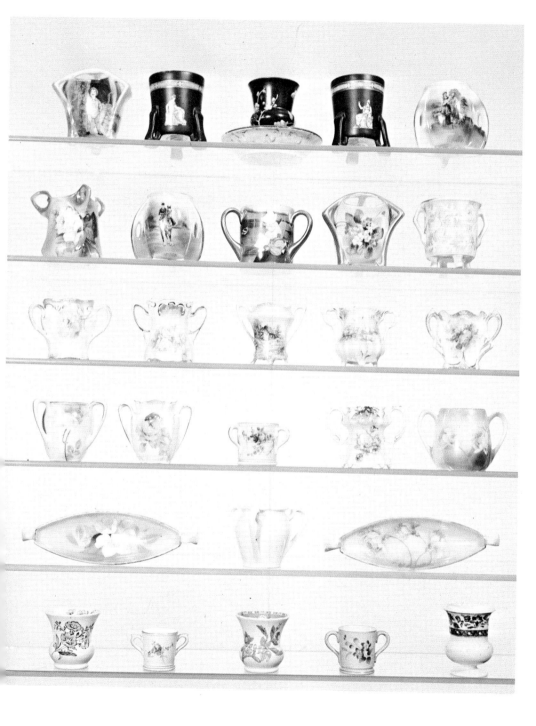

PLATE VIII

FIRST ROW

Negro Boy, Milk Glass _____Boul., pl. 158
Hand with Fan, Milk Glass _____Mill. O, pl. 182
Scrolled Shell (Cornucopia) _____Boul., pl. 226

SECOND ROW

Chieftain Head, Milk Glass _____Boul., pl. 60
Bees, Black Milk Glass _____Boul., pl. 18
Corn, Milk Glass _____Mill. O., pl. 167

THIRD ROW

Flute, Marigold Carnival Glass _____Boul., pl. 54
Kittens, Marigold Carnival Glass _____Boul., pl. 56
Kittens, Blue Carnival Glass __ _____Boul., pl. 56
Flute, Purple Carnival Glass _____Boul., pl. 54

FOURTH ROW

*Blue Barrel, Milk Glass
Square Footed, Milk Glass _____Mill. O, pl. 196
Ribbed Leaf and Scroll, Milk Glass
*Painted Milk Glass

FIFTH ROW

*Painted Barrel, Milk Glass
Trough, Milk Glass
*Painted Flower, Milk Glass

SIXTH ROW

*Catherine, Milk Glass
Beaded Belt, Milk Glass _____Mill. O, pl. 159
*Painted Roses, Milk Glass, Rests on Wood Base
*Lamar
Tramp's Shoe _____Mill. O, pl. 27

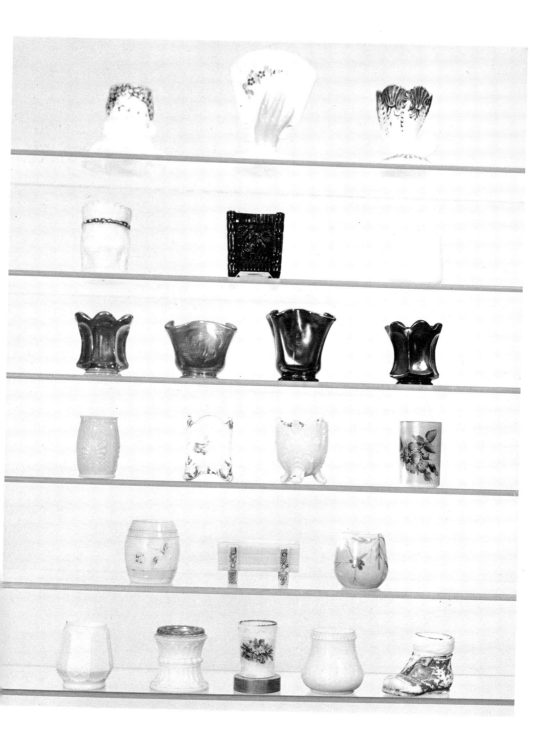

PLATE IX

There are no manufacturers' marks on these first three rows.

FOURTH ROW
Second from Left, R. C. Carmen, Bavaria
Third from Left, Welmar, Germany

FIFTH ROW
Far Right, Bavaria

SIXTH ROW
Far Left, Rosenthal, Bavaria

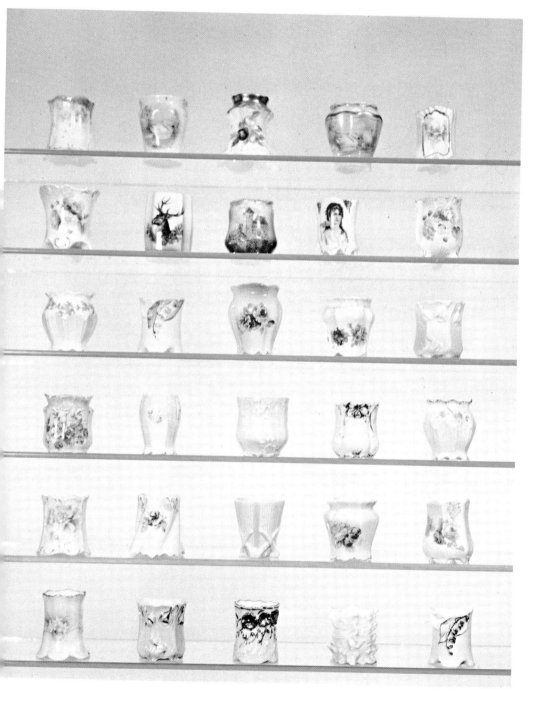

PLATE X

FIRST ROW
Clown
Pedestal Base
Elf
Frowning Face/Smiling Face
Clown

SECOND ROW
R. G. Versailles, Bavaria
Rosenthal, Bavaria
No Markings
M-Z, Austria
No Markings

THIRD ROW
No Markings
No Markings
Dicken's Day, England
Austria
Germany

None of the items in the fourth and fifth rows have manufacturers' marks.

SIXTH ROW
Three Crown, Germany
No Markings
No Markings
Germany
Germany

PLATE XI

FIRST ROW

Holly Amber _____Herr.
Green Croesus, Riverside Glass Co. _____Kamm IV, p. 112
Purple Croesus, Riverside Glass Co., Wellsville, W. Va., 1897
Holly Amber, Clear, Greentown Glass Co. _____Herr.

SECOND ROW

Royal Oak, Northwood Glass Co.,
      Martins Ferry, Ohio, 1899 _____Kamm V, p. 86
*Dorothy
Flora, Beaumont Glass Co., Martins Ferry, Ohio, 1898___Kamm V. p. 106
Flower and Pleat _____Pet. II, p. 11-R
* Royal Ivy, Northwood Glass Co., 1889 _____Kamm V, p. 87

THIRD ROW

Iris with Meander, Maker and Date Unknown _____Kamm VI, p. 63
Iris with Meander
Iris with Meander
Iris with Meander

FOURTH ROW

Esther, Riverside Glass Co., 1896 _____Kamm V, p. 54
Honeycomb with Flower Rim, Greentown, Ind. _____Kamm II, p. 117

FIFTH ROW

Jasper Ware
Sanded Copper Luster
Copper Luster
Wedgwood

SIXTH ROW

Brilliant, Riverside Glass Co., 1895 _____Boul., pl. 28
Heisey's No. 1235, Heisey _____Kamm VII, pl. 34
Daisy/Button (Amber Flash) _____Kamm V, p. 145
Britannic, McKee Glass Co., 1893 _____Kamm IV, p. 71
*Margarite

PLATE XII

FIRST ROW
Three Handles
Three Handles
On Brass and Wire Stand
Three Handles
Three Handles, Germany

SECOND ROW
Two Handles
Three Handles
Three Handles, Germany
Three Handles, Germany
Two Handles

THIRD ROW
No Markings
No Markings
Bavaria
No Markings

FOURTH ROW
Third from Left, "Arms of Dundee," Three Handles
Others are unmarked.

FIFTH ROW
Indented Star, Two Handles
D & C, France
Neo Classic Scene, Three Handles
Favorite, Bavaria
"Picks," Cigars Tied With White Ribbon

SIXTH ROW
No markings for this row.

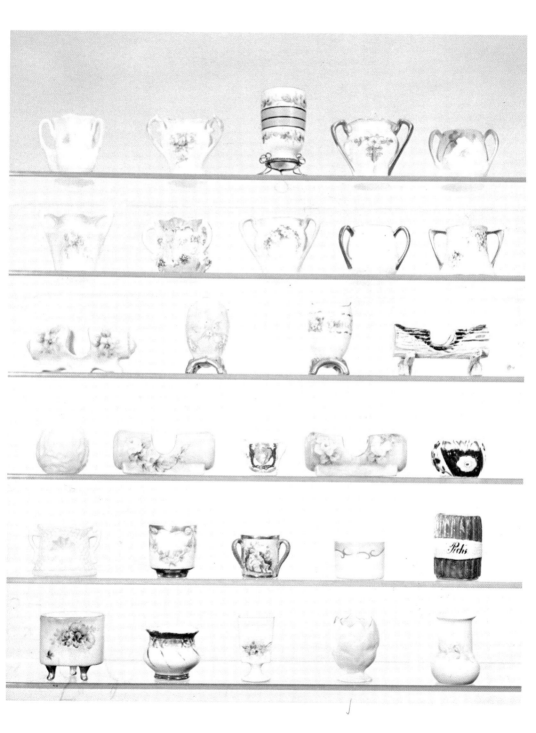

PLATE XIII

FIRST ROW
Parian
Bisque
Bisque, Impressed (7618)

SECOND ROW
Bisque
Bisque
Bisque, Impressed (5645)

THIRD ROW
Bisque, Impressed (10286)
Majolica, Embossed London Bridge G, 5338
Bisque

FOURTH ROW
Bisque, Impressed (465 F)
Porcelain
Porcelain

FIFTH ROW
Porcelain, Pigs at the Trough
Bisque
Porcelain, Pig and Egg

SIXTH ROW
Pig, Face in Stump
Pigs and Hat
Pig Playing Organ Grinder

PLATE XIV

FIRST ROW
Dog Soapstone, Signed China

SECOND ROW
Soapstone, Foliage Decor, Signed China

THIRD ROW
Soapstone, Three Carved Crows, Signed China

FOURTH ROW
Soapstone, Three Monkeys, Signed China

FIFTH ROW
Soapstone, Carved Foliage, Signed China
Unpolished Alabaster
Soapstone, Foliage Decor, Signed China

SIXTH ROW
All three are polished alabaster.

PLATE XV

FIRST ROW

Daisy/Button
Stars and Stripes, Milk Glass
Ribbed

SECOND ROW

Diamond Point
Diamond Point
Daisy/Button, Milk Glass
Daisy/Button
Diamond Point, English Hob on Rim

THIRD ROW

Thousand Eye
Fine Rib
Americana

FOURTH ROW

Blown
Bristol
Cobalt

FIFTH AND SIXTH ROWS

Porcelain and Semi-Porcelain

PLATE XVI

FIRST ROW
Poole Silver Co., Launton, Mass.
James W. Tufts, Boston, Mass.
Derby Silver Co.
James W. Tufts
Van Bergh Silver Plate Co., Rochester, N. Y.

SECOND ROW
Name worn too badly to read
Derby Silver Co.
Meriden Silver Plate Co.
Aurora Silver Plate
No Markings

THIRD ROW
Rockford Silver Plate Co.
Peru
No Markings
Mexico
Rogers Smith and Co., Meriden, Conn.

FOURTH ROW
Forbes Silver Co.
Rogers Smith and Co.
Meriden Silver Plate Co.
Reed and Barton
Aurora Silver Plate

FIFTH ROW
Brass with Inlay of Mother of Pearl
Holman Silver Plate
Enamel Decoration, E. G. Webster and Son, Brooklyn, N. Y.
No. 346
Acme Silver Plate Co., Boston, Mass.
No Markings

SIXTH ROW
Aluminum, Weighted Base
Brass, Scroll in Mid-Section
Cloisonne
Copper, Three Dog Heads
Copper and Brass, Linton, England
Cloisonne
W. M. F. N. (William F. Newhall), Lynn, Mass.

PLATE XVII

FIRST ROW
Round, Two Rows Vertical Fine Cut, Four Rows Vertical Notch Prism
Square, Fine Cut on Two Sides
Round, Pedestal Base, Honeycomb
Square, Vertical Notch Prisms
Square, Church Window, Diamond Point Above

SECOND ROW
Round, Three Panels Alternate, Notch Prism, Daisy
Impressed Snow Drop
Round, Notched Base, Top Center Three Rows of Block
Hexagon, Leaf in Panel Vertical Notch
Round, Two Panel Pinwheel, Vertical Notch

THIRD ROW
Flat Diamond Lower Half, Top Hexagon Flute
Round, Two Panels of Two Vertical Notched Bull's Eye, Two Panels
    Pinwheel
English Hobnail and Fan *Cut*
Two Panels Notched Stars
Vertical Notch

FOURTH ROW
Diamond Point Hobstar Band
Belted Diamond Point and Hobstar
Vertical Notch Prism
Alternate Panels of Bull's Eye and Vertical Notch Prisms
Leaf with Cane and Diamond Point

FIFTH ROW
Flat Diamond
Vertical Notch Prism, Belted by Flat Diamond
Cross and Fan
Tapered Star and Fan
Tapered Vertical Notch Prism

SIXTH ROW
Pentagon
Three Panel Star, Diamond Vertical Notch Prism
S-Shape Vertical Rib
Ovate Panels
Bull's Eye, Diamond Vertical Notch Prism

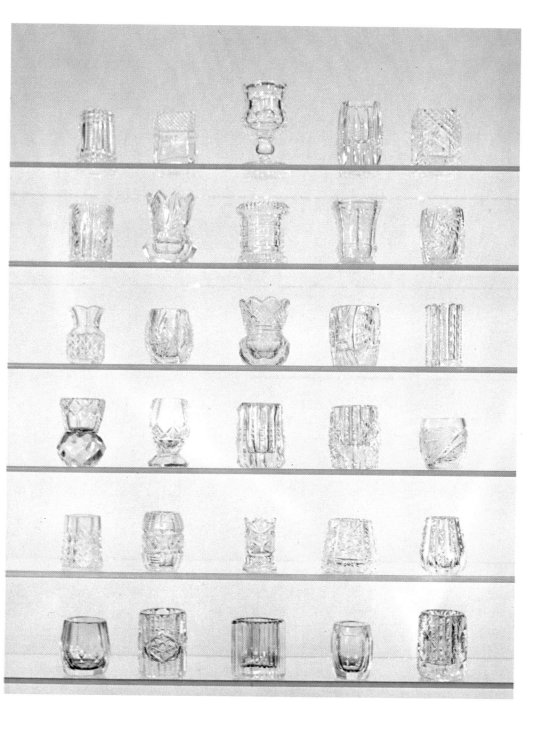

PLATE XVIII

FIRST ROW
Tapered Vertical Notch Prism
Cranberry to Clear Cut Overlay
Square, Six Petal Flower

SECOND ROW
False Base Eight Point Star
Pedestal Bull's Eye and Star
Leaf and Bud

THIRD ROW
Two Daisies
Red to Clear Cut Overlay
Two Handles, Engraved Flower

FOURTH ROW
Six Panel Diamond in Fine Cut
Blue to Clear Cut Overlay, Baccarat
Four Panels Alternate, Five Vertical Thumbprint-Diamond Point and Fan

FIFTH ROW
Honey Comb and Star
Square, Strawberry and Fan
Vertical Notch Prism

SIXTH ROW
Flat Diamond and Fan
Belted Urn
Tapered Star and Fan

PLATE XIX

FIRST ROW
Embossed, Forget Me Not

SECOND ROW
Sanded, Applied Flowers
Sanded, Applied Flowers
Luster, Sanded, Applied Flowers

THIRD ROW
Boy's Head, Embossed
Lily of the Valley/Butterfly

FOURTH ROW
Woman's Bust, Transfer
Souvenir (Battle Creek Sanitarium)
Flower

FIFTH ROW
Two Handles at Top
Two Handles at Top, Sanded, Applied Flowers
Two Handles at Top

SIXTH ROW
H. P. Lilacs
Applied Flowers

PLATE XX

FIRST ROW

*Carnation
*Waterford
Jefferson's No. 270, Jefferson Glass Co., Circa 1900_____Kamm VII, p. 45
Double Pinwheel, Maker Unknown, Circa 1890 _____Kamm IV, p. 141
Thousand Eye, Richards and Hartley, Circa 1870 _____Kamm I, p. 18

SECOND ROW

Scroll with Acanthus, Central Glass Co., Circa 1880 ____Kamm III, p. 68
Clover, Richards and Hartley, Flint Glass Co., 1891____Kamm VIII, p. 44
*Marge
Heisey's No. 300 (Colonial), 1897 _____Kamm VIII, pl. 90
Empire, McKee Glass Co., Jeannette, Pa. _____Kamm III, p. 40

THIRD ROW

Jefferson's No. 251, Jefferson Glass Co., Circa 1900 ____Kamm VII, p. 46
Cob, Richards and Hartley, 1888 _____Kamm II, p. 19
Circle Double, Jefferson Glass Co. _____Pet. II, p. 9-J
Tepee, George A. Duncan and Sons, 1894 _____Kamm II, p. 78
Daisy/Button

FOURTH ROW

Near Cut Colonial, Cambridge Glass Co.,
      Beaver Falls, Pa. _____ _____Kamm VIII, p. 45
Colonial (Twenty-eight Point Star In Base)
Columbia, Beaumont Glass Co., 1893 _____Kamm VII, p. 25
*Inverted Church Windows
Austria, Indiana Tumbler and Glass Co., 1897 _____Kamm II, p. 43

FIFTH ROW

Diamond Lattice, Maker and Date Unknown _____Kamm II, p. 77
Wedding Bells, Fostoria Glass Co.,
      Moundsville, W. Va., Circa 1900 _____Kamm IV, p. 113
Swag with Bracket, Maker and Date Unknown _____Kamm I, p. 86
Strawberry with Fan
*Zipper Edge Panels

SIXTH ROW

*Thomas
Barrel, Bryce, Higbee and Co. _____Kamm VIII, pl. 32
Strawberry with Fan
*Corset Colonial
Double Arch, U. S. Glass Co., Circa 1900 _____Kamm VII, p. 59

PLATE XXI

FIRST ROW

Bellaire, Bellaire Goblet Co., Findlay, Ohio, Circa 1890__Kamm V, p. 114
Button Arches (Clam Broth)
Rainbow, McKee, 1894 _____Kamm VI, pl. 89
Lacy Medallion (Clam Broth), U. S. Glass Co., Circa 1890__Kamm I, p. 106
Columned Thumbprint, Maker Unknown, Late 1800s ____Kamm V, p. 71

SECOND ROW

Daisy with Button
✗ Fancy Loop, A. H. Heisey, 1897 _____Kamm II, p. 97
Twin Snow Shoe, Maker Unknown, Circa 1890 _____Kamm VIII, p. 54
Pineapple and Fan, A. H. Heisey, 1897 _____Kamm II, p. 93
Brazilian, Fostoria Glass Co.,
        Moundsville, W. Va., 1898 _____Kamm VII, p. 33

THIRD ROW

X-Ray, Riverside Glass Co., 1896 _____Kamm V, p. 136
Teasel, Bryce Bros., Pittsburgh, Pa., Circa 1870 _____Metz I, p. 68
Stippled Star, Maker Unknown, Circa 1890 _____Kamm I, p. 103
Bull's Eye and Fan, Maker and Date Unknown _____Kamm I, p. 58
Acanthus Leaf, Maker and Date Unknown _____Kamm II, p. 53

FOURTH ROW

Snow Flake, Maker and Date Unknown _____Kamm II, p. 104
Lacy Floral, Maker and Date Unknown _____Kamm V, p. 114
Zipper Slash, George A. Duncan and Sons, 1893 _____Kamm III, p. 83
Ribbed Thumbprint, Northwood Glass Co.,
        Wheeling, W. Va., After 1900 _____Kamm IV, p. 106
*Vivian

FIFTH ROW

Bevel Star, Flint Glass Co., Findlay, Ohio, Circa 1890 ____Kamm II, p. 70
Reward, National Glass Co., Circa 1900 _____Kamm V, p. 109
X-Ray, Riverside Glass Co. _____Kamm V, p. 136
✗ Sunbeam, McKee, 1898 _____Kamm IV, p. 76
Little Gem, Maker and Date Unknown _____Kamm VII, p. 60

SIXTH ROW

*Jessie
*Traci
Ruby Diamond, Maker and Date Unknown _____Kamm II, p. 93
Bull's Eye and Daisy, Maker Unknown, Circa 1890 _____Metz I, p. 214
Doric, McKee, 1896 _____Kamm I, p. 73

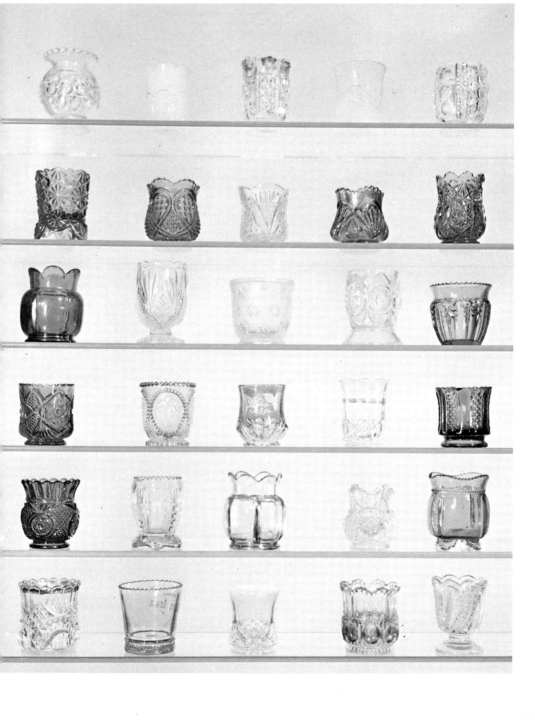

PLATE XXII

FIRST ROW

Panama, U. S. Glass Co., Circa 1890 _____Kamm II, p. 49
*Pinched Star
Swag with Bracket, Maker and Date Unknown _____Kamm I, p. 86
Serrated Spear Points, Circa 1880 _____Mill. O II, pl. 74
Majestic, McKee, Circa 1890 _____Kamm II, p. 71

SECOND ROW

Button and Star Panel _____Pet. I, p. 24-B
Daisy/Button, Metal Bands
Beatty's Honeycomb, A. J. Beatty and Co.,
    Tiffin, Ohio, Circa 1880 _____Boul., pl. 16
*Daisy/Button Band and Base
Petticoat _____Pet. I, p. 35-J

THIRD ROW

Colonial
Thousand Eye, Richards and Hartley,
    Tarentum, Pa., Circa 1888 _____Kamm I, p. 18
Manhattan, U. S. Glass Co., Circa 1900 _____Kamm VI, p. 44
Daisy/Button, A. J. Beatty, Circa 1886 _____Kamm V, p. 112
Daisy/Button, A. J. Beatty, Circa 1886 _____Kamm V, p. 112

FOURTH ROW

Barrel
Strawberry Jar, Maker and Date Unknown _____Kamm VII, p. 17
Wreath and Shell, Albany Art Glass,
    Model Flint Glass Co., Albany, Ohio _____Herr.
Sunken Teardrop, Maker and Date Unknown _____Kamm IV, p. 26
Daisy and Button Urn

FIFTH Row

Barrel
Swirl and Star Base _____Pet. I, p. 41-I
Carmen, Fostoria Glass Co., Moundsville, W. Va.,
    Circa 1896 _____Kamm V, p. 121
Sunk Daisy, Co-Operative Flint, Beaver Falls, Pa.,
    Circa 1898 _____Kamm III, p. 89
Moon and Star Variant

SIXTH ROW

*Kent, Three Handles, Two Ovate Panels Divided by Deep Slash Between
    Handles
*Nine Panel Colonial, Twelve Point Star in Base
S-Repeat, National Glass Co., Circa 1903 _____Kamm IV, p. 115
Barred Hobnail, Brilliant Glass Work,
    Brilliant, Ohio, Circa 1888 _____Kamm I, p. 113
*Randy, Square Base, Round at Top

PLATE XXIII

FIRST ROW

Three in One, Maker Unknown, Circa 1800 _____Kamm IV, p. 74
Button Arches (Ruby Flash), Duncan and Miller Glass Co.
  Circa 1900 _____Kamm I, p. 111
The Prize, National Glass Co., Circa 1900 _____Kamm V, p. 67
Etched Rabbit (Ruby Flash)
Cane Shield, In Metal Frame of Corn and Stalks,
  Maker Unknown _____Kamm V, p. 138

SECOND ROW

Late Jacob's Ladder, U. S. Glass Co., Circa 1900 _____Kamm I, p. 98
*Cherry Sprig, Eighteen Point Star in Base
xRuby Thumbprint, Adams & Co., Circa 1890 _____Kamm I, p. 104
Ladder in Diamond, Maker and Date Unknown _____Kamm VIII, p. 42
*Stippled Leaf in Wishbone

THIRD ROW

Regal, U. S. Glass Co., Circa 1906 _____Kamm VI, p. 51
Button Arches with Frosted Band (Ruby Flash)
Lacy Medallion (Ruby Flash), U. S. Glass Co., Circa 1890_Kamm I, p. 106
Heisey's No. 1225 _____Kamm VII, pl. 33

FOURTH ROW

Rainbow, McKee, Circa 1894 _____Kamm VI, pl. 89
Duncan and Sons' No. 40, George A. Duncan and Sons,
  Circa 1900 _____Kamm VII, pl. 18
National Eureka, National Glass Co., Circa 1900 _____Kamm V, p. 69
*Joyce
Adam's Saxon, Bakwell, Pears and Co., Pittsburgh, Pa. __Kamm III, p. 8

FIFTH ROW

+Button Arch
Duncan and Miller's No. 30, After 1894 _____Kamm VII, pl. 25
Cordova, O'Hara Glass Co., Pittsburgh, Pa., 1890;
  U. S. Glass Co., After 1898 _____Kamm I, p. 105
Wild Bouquet, Possibly Northwood, Uniontown, Pa.,
  Circa 1910 _____Bra.
Thompson's No. 77, Thompson Glass Co., Circa 1892 ____Kamm V, p. 82

SIXTH ROW

Bead and Scroll, Maker and Date Unknown _____Kamm II, p. 112
Scroll with Cane Band, W. Virginia Glass Co.,
  Martins Ferry, Ohio, Circa 1895 _____Kamm III, p. 92
*Plain George
Portland, Portland Glass Co., Portland, Me. _____Kamm I, p. 107
xRoyal, Co-Operative Flint Glass Co., Beaver Falls, Pa.,
  Circa 1893 _____Kamm VI, p. 23

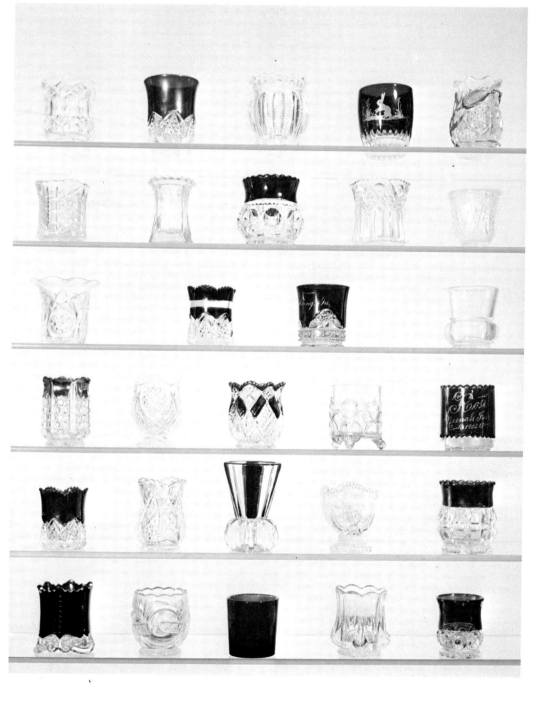

PLATE XXIV

FIRST ROW
Daisy/Button
Colonial, Signed Pres., Cut
Blue Satin, Enamel Flowers on Flange
Flattened Diamond Sunburst, Maker Unknown,
　　Circa 1800 _____Kamm II, p. 54
Waffle and Fine Cut, Maker and Date Unknown _____Kamm II, p. 99

SECOND ROW
Jefferson's No. 270, Jefferson Glass Co. _____Kamm VII, p. 45
Concave Almond, Maker Unknown, Circa 1893 _____Kamm VIII, p. 39
Plain Scalloped Panel _____Kamm I, p. 81
Overall Diamond, Maker Unknown, Circa 1900 _____Kamm VII, p. 32
Printed Hobnail

THIRD ROW
Ladders, Larentum Glass Co., Larentum, Pa., Circa 1901__Kamm V, p. 79
Ribbed Opal, A. J. Beatty and Co., Circa 1888 _____Kamm VI, p. 55
Duncan's No. 42, Duncan and Miller, Circa 1898 _____Kamm V, p. 70
Ribbed Opal
Atlas, Bryce Bros., Circa 1889 _____Kamm II, p. 15

FOURTH ROW
Pointed Gothic, Maker and Date Unknown _____Kamm VI, p. 32
*Scalloped Skirt
Honeycomb with Flower Rim, Circa 1903 _____Kamm II, p. 117
Duncan's No. 2000, George A. Duncan and Sons,
　　Circa 1892 _____Kamm VIII, p. 184
Gaelic, Maker Unknown, Circa 1900 _____Kamm IV, p. 122

FIFTH ROW
Overall Hob, Circa 1880 _____Kamm V, p. 107
Hobnail with Line Band, Maker and Date Unknown ____Kamm VII, p. 24
*Columned Snowflake
Spear Point Band, Maker and Date Unknown _____Kamm VII, p. 31
Flattened Hob in Diamond, Pressed Opal Top _____Boul., pl. 184

SIXTH ROW
Daisy and Button Band, Maker and Date Unknown ____Kamm VI, p. 20
Whirligig, U. S. Glass Co., Circa 1898 _____Kamm II, p. 103
Opalescent Hob, Rim Base
*Inverted Eye
Ribbed Spiral, Model Flint Glass Co. _____Herr., pl. 312

PLATE XXV

FIRST ROW

Panelled Palm, U. S. Glass Co., Circa 1890 _____Metz II, p. 68
*Ralph
*Susan
*Scalloped Skirt
Ellipes, Maker Unknown, Circa 1890 _____Boul., pl. 93

SECOND ROW

George Duncan and Sons, No. 308, Circa 1890 _____Kamm V, pl. 31
Tepee, George Duncan and Sons, 1894 _____Kamm II, p. 78
Regal, Maker Unknown, 1901 _____Kamm V, p. 68
Lacy Medallion, U. S. Glass Co., Circa 1890 _____Kamm I, p. 106
Americana

THIRD ROW

U. S. Rib, U. S. Glass Co., Circa 1900 _____Kamm VII, p. 42
Daisy/Button Urn
Ribbed Opal, A. J. Beatty and Co. _____Kamm VIII, p. 32
Americana
Plain Scalloped Panel, U. S. Glass Co., 1907 _____Kamm I, p. 81

FOURTH ROW

Night Light
Near Cut No. 2651, Cambridge Glass Co. _____Kamm VIII, p. 40
*Brass Ring
Scalloped Swirl, U. S. Glass Co., 1891 _____Kamm VI, p. 26
Regal, Advertised Montgomery Ward Catalog, 1901_____Kamm V, p. 68

FIFTH ROW

Prince of Wales Plume, A. H. Heisey, 1900 _____Kamm I, p. 115
Regal, 1901 _____Kamm V, p. 68
Virginia (Banded Portland), U. S. Glass Co. _____Kamm II, p. 89
Star in Bull's Eye, U. S. Glass Co., 1907 _____Kamm I, p. 100
Heavy Panelled Grape, Possibly Sandwich Glass Co. ____Kamm III, p. 61

SIXTH ROW

Inverted Thumbprint
Pleated Oval, Maker Unknown, 1898 _____Kamm VIII, p. 34
*Frosted Barrel with Brass Bands
Daisy/Button Urn
*Albert

PLATE XXVI

FIRST ROW

Swirl Opal and Clear _____Herr., pl. 325
Sunburst Variant
*Diamond Point Heart
Box in Box, Date and Maker Unknown _____Kamm VI, p. 65

SECOND ROW

Hobnail, Band Top, Panel Base
Cobalt Set in Metal Frame
Bundle of Sticks
*Tree with Thumbprint
*Upside-Down Grape

THIRD ROW

Hobnail _____Herr., pl. 322
Frosted Hobnail
Hobnail

FOURTH ROW

Ruby Flash, Clear Ring Base
Inverted Thumbprint
*Six Panel
*Ruby Flash Horizontal Bars
Honeycomb

FIFTH ROW

*Fan
*Printed Hobnail
Inverted Thumbprint
Three Face; None were made with original pieces,
        Circa 1930 _____Kamm III, p. 11
*Mary Lou

SIXTH ROW

Honeycomb
*Myrtle
Bundle of Sticks
Daisy and Button
*Green Apple

PLATE XXVII

FIRST ROW
Loving Cup, Two Handles
*Panelled Honeycomb and Diamond Point Block
Mercury
Loving Cup, Three Handles
Ruby Flash, Two Handles

SECOND ROW
*Diamond Point Skirt, Two Handles
*Purple Pansy, Three Handles, K Impressed in Base
Rising Sun, Three Handles, Maker and Date Unknown __Kamm II, p. 61

THIRD ROW
Signed Heisey
Silver Rim Lion Head
*Double Panel Swirl with Rope, Silver Base
*Silver Rim Urn
Hawaiian Lei, Signed Higbee, Circa 1880 _____Mill. G I, pl. 46

FOURTH ROW
*Dallas, "RADEBACGH" Embossed in Base
Blazing Cornucopia, Maker and Date Unknown _____Kamm VI, p. 29
*Wichita, Two Handles
Blazing Cornucopia
Double Church Windows, Maker and Date Unknown __Kamm IV, p. 115

FIFTH ROW
Double Star in Bull's Eye, U. S. Glass Co., 1907 _____Kamm I, p. 100
Star of Bethlehem, Two Handles,
        Cambridge Glass Co., 1909 _____Kamm VII, p. 67
*Brass Frame Urn
*Church Windows and Diamonds
Double Gloved Hand, Maker Unknown, Circa 1900 ____Kamm VI, p. 59

SIXTH ROW
Double Heisey, Signed, Stamped "PAT APL'D FOR"
Heisey, Signed
Knobby Bull's Eye _____Metz I, p. 214

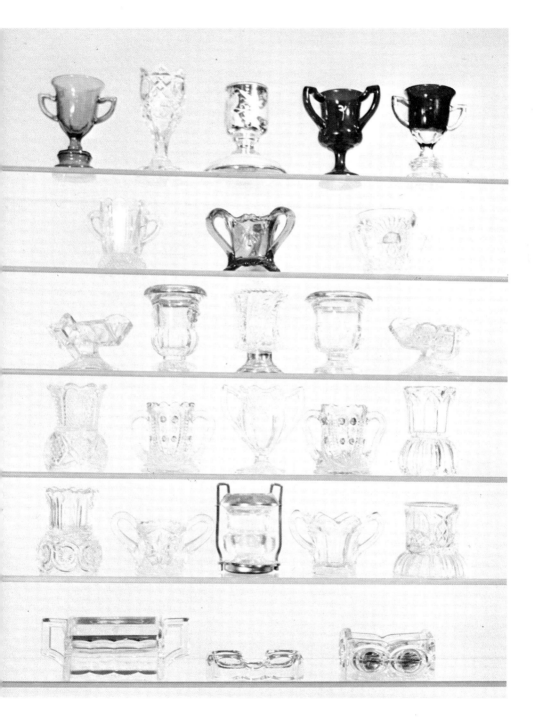

PLATE XXVIII

FIRST ROW

There are no manufacturers' marks on any of these items.

SECOND ROW

Green M in Wreath, Nippon
Japan
No markings on the rest.

THIRD ROW

No Markings
Two Handles, Green Crown, Nippon
Three Handles, Green Maple Leaf, Nippon
Blue NPMC, Nippon
No Markings

FOURTH ROW

Lithophane in Bottom
No Markings
Red Chinese Marking
Japan
No Markings

FIFTH ROW

No Markings
No Markings
Markings Obliterated
Blue Wilhelmina, Porcelain T, Standing Lion
No Markings

SIXTH ROW

No Markings
Veuve Pottery
Green Crown Victoria, Czechoslovakia NU
No Markings
Japan

PLATE XXIX

During the latter part of the nineteenth century many novelty items, such as toothpick holders, match safes, and candy containers, were produced. Since it is often difficult to distinguish one from the other, I decided to leave the items unclassified.

FIRST ROW

Charley Chaplin
Good Luck Horseshoe
Domino
Kewpie

SECOND ROW

Kitten on Pillow _____Boul., pl. 57; Lee P, pl. 186
Indian Maid with Basket _____Metz II, p. 216
Squirrel and Tree Stump

THIRD ROW

Dog and Cart
Kneeling Cherubs
Dog and Hat _____Metz II, p. 214; Boul., pl. 89

PLATE XXX

FIRST ROW

Monkey and Hat _____Boul., pl. 154
Money on Tree Stump _____Boul., pl. 153
Saddle _____Metz II, p. 218; Boul., pl. 207
Owl _____Boul., pl. 165; Lee V, pl. 105
Log House, Tecumseh _____Lee V, pl. 105
Book
Old Woman _____Herr.

SECOND ROW

Gypsy Kettle, Daisy/Button
Dolphin
Nautilus Shell
Elephant Head
Horse and Cart

THIRD ROW

Cherubs Holding Barrel _____Lee P, pl. 186
Picture Frame, Signed R&M _____Herr.
Crane in Reeds
Dolphin with Seashells
Frog and Lily Pad _____Boul., pl. 115
Man with Pack on Back
Fleur de Lis _____Lee V, pl. 105